The Beano and Dandy comic heroes, like every youngster, found the 80s a great decade to be growing up in. Kylie and Jason were on the telly every weekday in 'Neighbours', E.T was a must-see in the cinema and big Frank Bruno was boxing for the World Title. The cool sounds of the eighties came from Bros, Adam Ant, Shakin' Stevens, Toyah...Whoa! Stop! There was just so much going on in this decade and all of it was influencing the Beano and Dandy story writers.

Jackie
PIN-UP SPECIAL

THE PICK OF THE POSTERS!

BOO-HOO-HOO! WHAT A LOVELY, MOVING FILM!

SOFTY WALTER

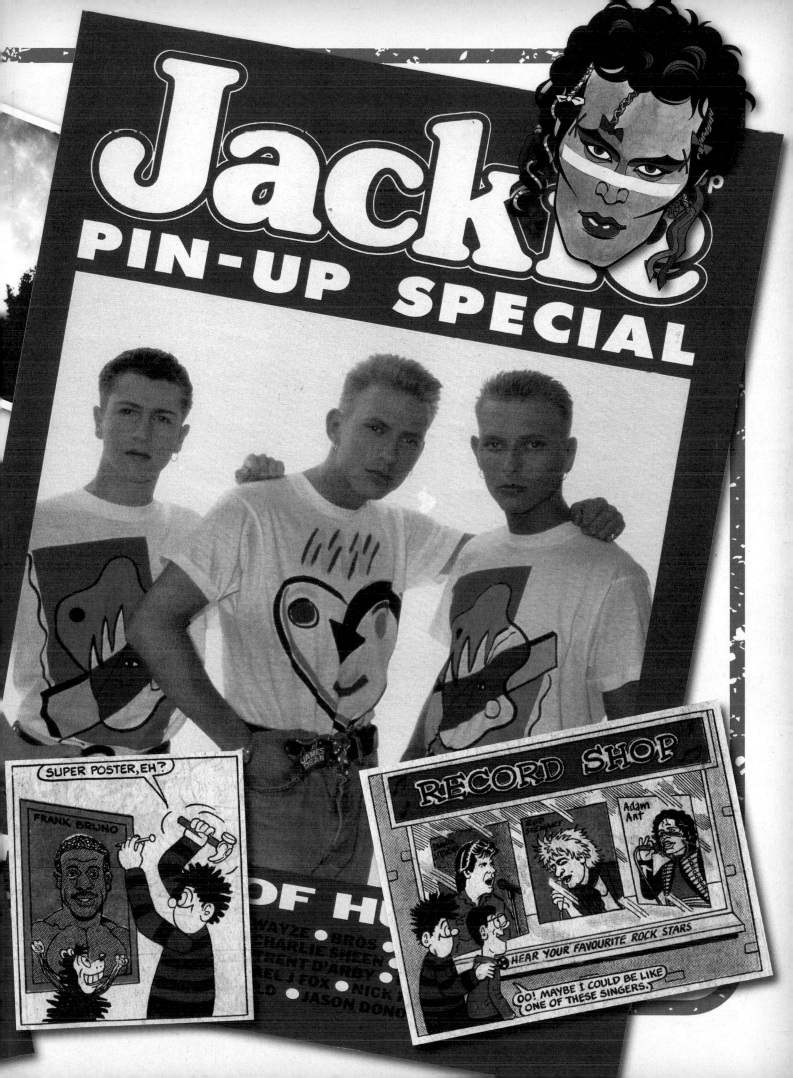

DENNIS the MENACE and GNASHER

The top schoolboy hero was the untameable rogue, Dennis the Menace. As always he was supported by his faithful, four legged companion, Gnasher. The 80s were very successful for the pair and they starred in some great stories inspired by the happenings of the times.

The pair would front Beano number 2000 in 1980, the first copy of the Beano Comic Library in 1982, the highest selling Beano Book ever in 1983 (554,000 copies sold) and the Beano 50th birthday issue in 1988. In between, in 1986, Gnasher would go missing in a story that made headlines in the national press and was reported on TV and radio. Yes, a busy little decade for our top heroes.

FROM "The BEANO"
DENNIS the Menace
1983

Dennis, Curly, Pie-face and Gnasher are the band DENNIS and the DINMAKERS! Their style of music is 'loud rock' where max volume is everything.

The Dinmakers starred in this good gag on the cover and back cover of the 1983 Dennis annual.

Film heroes were members of Dennis' fan club in 1980. The original Luke Skywalker from Star Wars, actor Mark Hamill, paid the 30p fee and he and son Nathan joined the red and black side. This excellent drawing was done at that time to promote the club.

Blue Jeans

No. 376 March 31, 1984
Every Monday

22p
IR 36p
(Inc. VAT)

Mike Read who fronted BBC's Saturday Superstore, models a Dennis jersey on the cover of top selling 80s mag Blue Jeans. You could send in to the mag for a pattern and knit one yourself – or pester your Gran into doing it. Millions of children were in front of the box every Saturday morning to watch this cult 80s tv show 'Superstore'. It was a time when Dennis Fan Club member Mike Read ruled.

READ ALL ABOUT–

GREAT GKNITS! DENNIS & GNASHER JUMPERS!

LIMAHL'S DREAM DAY!

What to do if you hate your hair!

Tut-tut! Tough nut!

What's wrong? Teeth long!

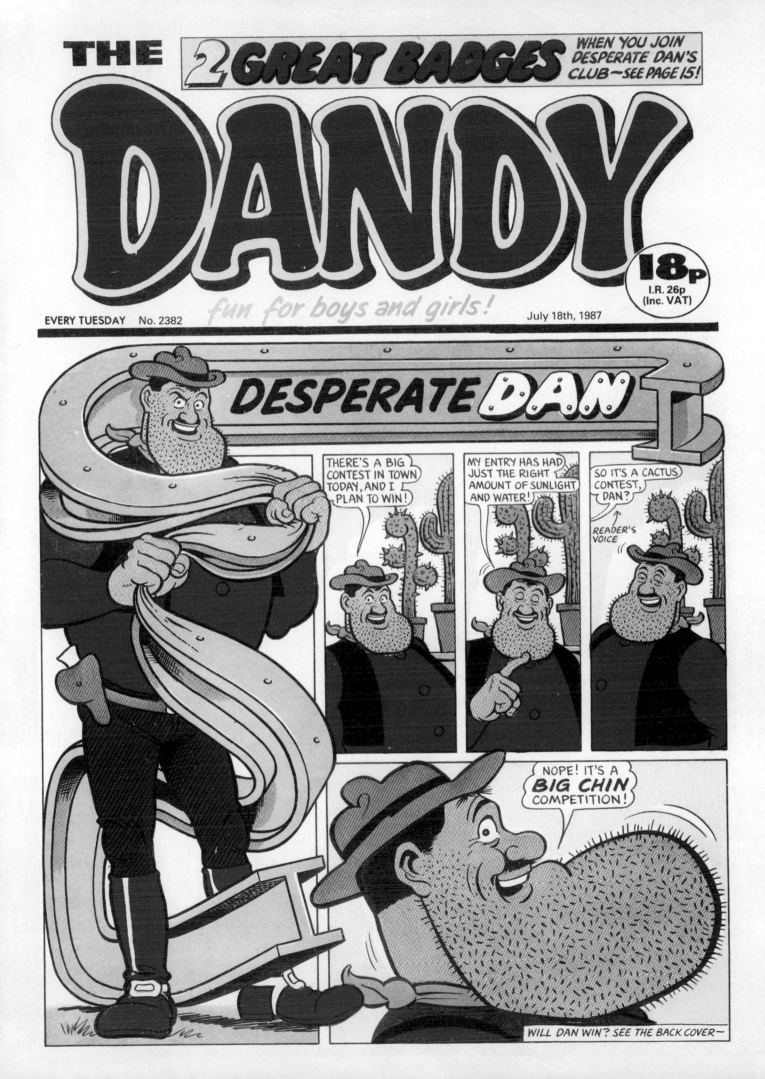

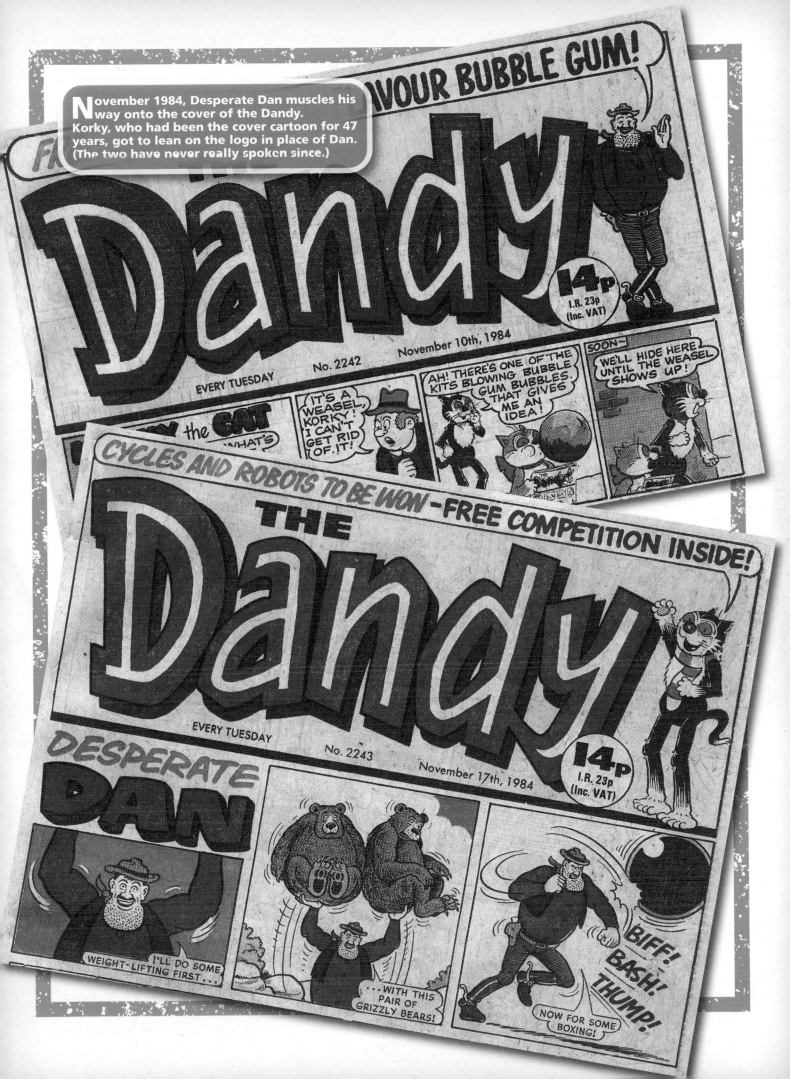

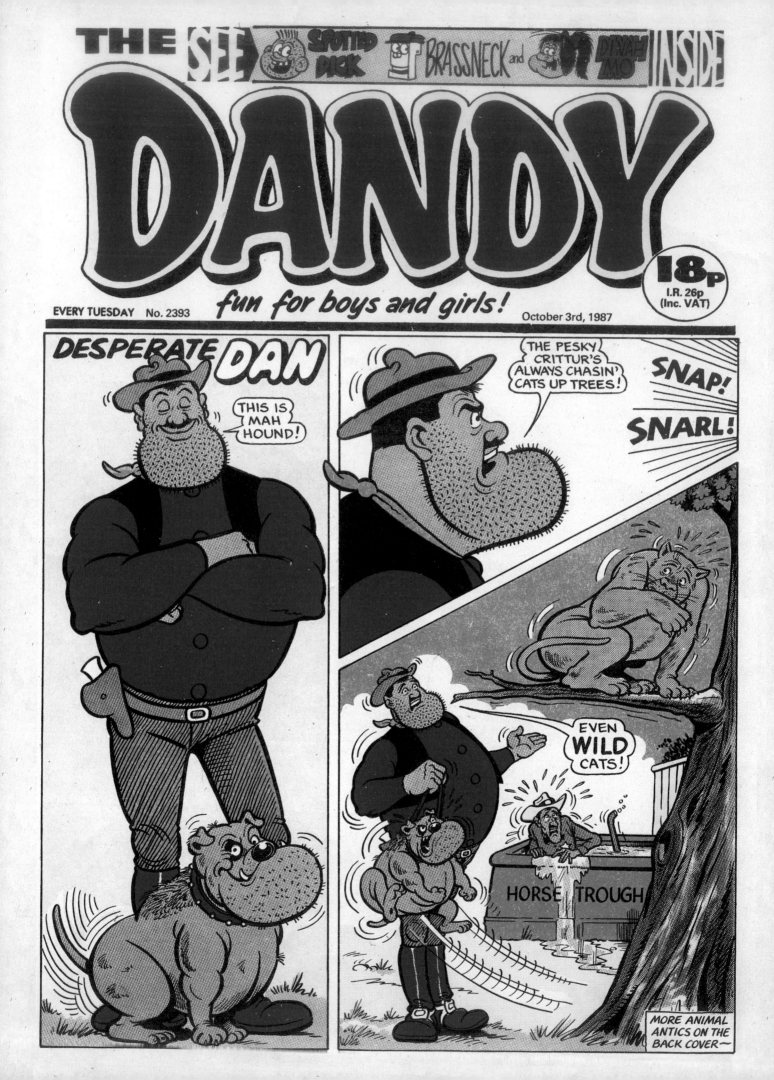

Readers were introduced to Desperate Dan's dog in the 80s. It was a pedigree Cactusville Cruncher, a breed notoriously difficult to train. Dan had really used his imagination and called it Dawg.
In 2001 Desperate Dan and Dawg were cast into giant bronze statues and given pride of place in the centre of their home city of Dundee, Scotland.

Olive's food does some good!

A silly goon with a balloon!

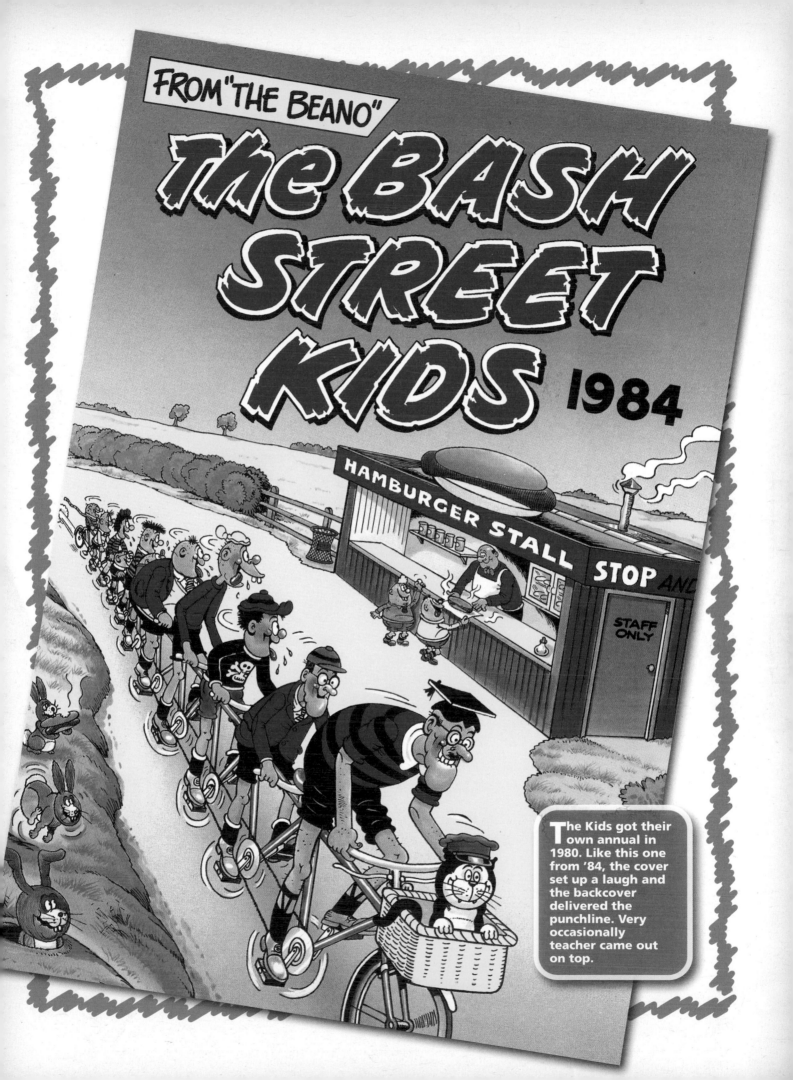

FOCUS ON FUN

SMIFFY WINNING THE SACK RACE AT THE SCHOOL SPORTS.

Roger's Dodge Clinic brought in hundreds of dodge requests each week to the Beano office. In true Roger style the office guys would try to dodge having to open so many bags of mail. In this photo young Craig uses the excuse that he was attacked by Gnasher while carrying the mail to his desk.(Looks more like Desperate Dan than Gnasher).

PRE-SCHOOL HEROES

CUDDLES and DIMPLES
the Dandy's terror toddlers.

Cuddles started life in the 80s comic, Nutty whereas Dimples had a page strip of his own in the Dandy. When the two comics joined forces in 1985 plans were made to combine the characters, and give them a double page to play around in.

This strip was produced especially for John Craven and his Newsround team visiting the Cuddles and Dimples artist, Barrie Appleby in his studio. The programme was flagging up the forthcoming 50th birthday of the Dandy comic in 1987.

IVY the TERRIBLE

Ivy was the brainchild of Beano editor, Alan Digby, who based the character on his real child, daughter Jane. This snap is of Jane as a toddler in the 80s – check the hair bunches, now you know where Ivy got them. Ivy could melt your heart with a smile one moment and have even Dennis the Menace quaking in his size sevens the next.

WATCH OUT, DENNIS and MINNIE!

IVY THE TERRIBLE IS AFTER YOU!

LOOK OUT FOR THE TODDLER TERROR IN "The BEANO" NEXT WEEK!

GHASTLY GHOSTIES

Dennis and Gnasher were obviously Ghost Buster fans.

CHAPTER ONE

GHOST BASHERS!

**BABY-FACE
FINLAYSON
EXTREMELY NAUGHTY
PERSON**
MADE A BIG SPLASH ROBBING A
BANK (IT WAS A RIVER BANK)
SLIPPED UP TRYING TO STEAL
A BANANA. STOLE SOME
INDIAN CURRY - BUT GOT HOT
UNDER THE COLLAR. STOLE A
CRAB FROM A FISH SHOP -
BUT GOT PINCHED! WANTED
FOR ARMED ROBBERY AND
ALSO LEGGED ROBBERY.

LAST PRE-SCHOOL HERO
BABY-FACE FINLAYSON

This pram powered crime starts with Boy George and
ends with the Police. Ah, I'm going to dig out my
original Sony Walkman and listen to an 80s cassette.

Rise surprise!

Only Min can be such a fan!

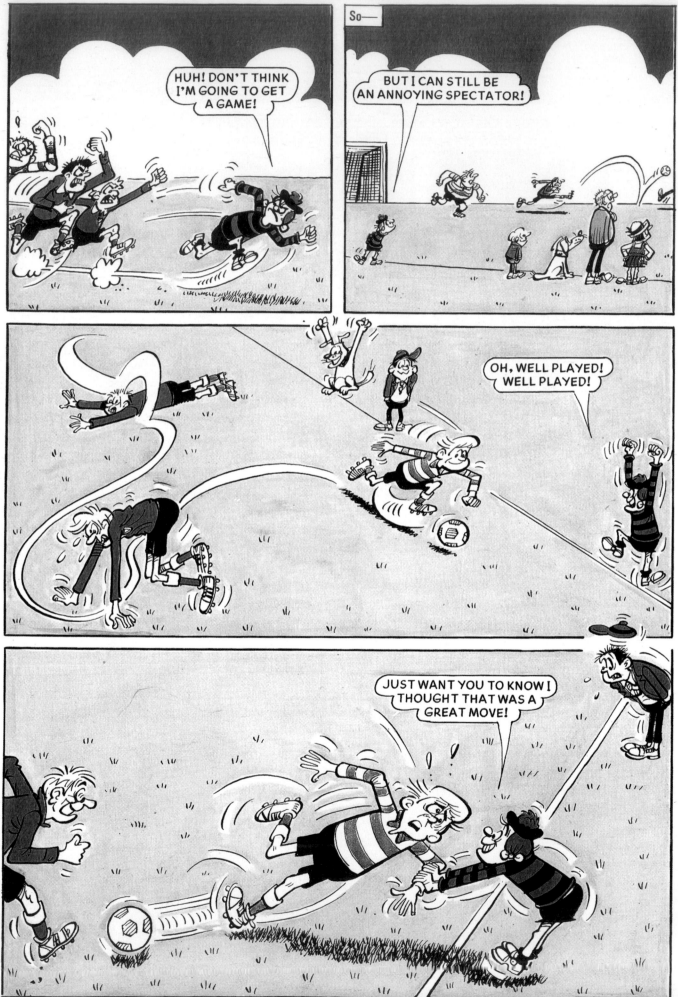

What a shame—end of game!

Battle of the Titans from the 50th birthday edition of The Dandy, 1987.